Conquer Year 5 English with CGP!

Ready to test the key facts and methods in Year 5 English? Once pupils have got to grips with all the content in our matching Year 5 English Knowledge Organiser, they can check how much they've learned with our Knowledge Retriever!

With bonus mixed practice quizzes and a full set of answers too, this book has everything Year 5 pupils need for English success!

CGP — still the best! ☺

Our sole aim here at CGP is to produce the highest quality books — carefully written, immaculately presented and dangerously close to being funny.

Then we work our socks off to get them out to you — at the cheapest possible prices.

Contents

Published by CGP.

Editors: Siân Butler, Robbie Driscoll, Nathan Mair, Georgina Paxman, James Summersgill

With thanks to Becca Lakin and Amanda MacNaughton for the proofreading.

With thanks to Alice Dent for the copyright research.

ISBN: 978 1 78908 965 3

Printed by Elanders Ltd, Newcastle upon Tyne. Clipart from Corel®

Based on the classic CGP style created by Richard Parsons.

Text, design, layout and original illustrations © Coordination Group Publications Ltd. (CGP) 2022 All rights reserved.

How to Use This Book

This book is split into the different topics that you'll learn about in Year 5 English. Every page in this book has a matching page in the Year 5 English **Knowledge Organiser**. Before you fill in the pages in this book, you should have learnt about the topic in your lessons at school and in the Knowledge Organiser. This is what you need to do:

1 Read the pages and fill in any dotted lines as you go. One dotted line means there's one word missing — sometimes you get given the first letter of the word and sometimes you don't.

Sometimes, there is more than one possible answer. You just need to write any word that could fill the gap.

Occasionally, you only have to fill in a single letter or part of a word.

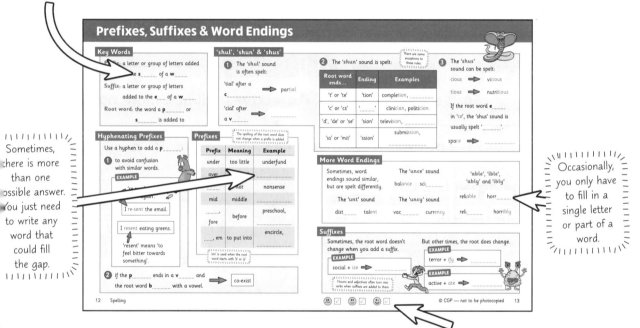

2 When you've finished, you can use the answers at the back of the book to check your work. Tick a smiley face to show how well you know the topic.

There are also **Quizzes** throughout the book:
- There is a quiz at the end of each section. These quizzes test a mix of content from the previous few pages. There is also a bigger quiz at the end, which covers everything from the book.
- Answers to the quizzes are at the back of the book. Write your score in the box at the end of each quiz.

Grammar Basics

Nouns

Nouns: words that name things

Noun Type	Used to name...	Examples
....	things you see, touch, smell or hear	mouse, cheese
Abstract	**i**............ or feelings	love, ...
....	groups of people or things	a swarm of bees

Verbs

Verbs: .... or being words

> Iris plays chess.

Verbs change depending on

w...... is doing the action.

> I walk.
>
> He .... They ....

Irregular verbs change in different ways. E.g. 'I am', 'she is'.

Adjectives

Adjectives tell you more about a ....

> the creaky stairs   a .... girl

M........... **verbs**: show how certain

or possible something is

> I might paint.

> I will paint.

Adverbs

Adverbs can describe:

1 .... She calmly slept in bed.

2 **Adjectives** He is .... loud.

3 **Adverbs** I spoke .... quietly.

Adverbs can also show possibility.
It is clearly lazy.

Pronouns

Pronouns

replace **n**...........

> Henrik baked
> a cake, and he
> decorated ......

Determiners

Determiners go in front of ....

They tell you if a noun is a general or specific thing.

I found a key.   I played my guitar.

I ate ...... orange.   I fixed this bike.

Relative Clauses

Relative clause: a subordinate clause

often introduced by a <u>relative</u> ....

> This is the best view <u>that</u> I've seen.

Relative clauses don't always

have a <u>relative</u> ....

> Geography is the subject <u>that</u> I enjoy the most.

You can remove the word 'that' and the sentence would still make sense.

Pronouns
avoid
repeating
'Henrik'
and 'cake'.

Relative pronouns

introduce relative ....

> I saw the girl
> <u>who</u> was crying.

Clauses

.... **<u>clause</u>**: has a

subject and a verb, and

makes sense on its own

Subordinate clause: gives

extra **i**.......................... but

doesn't make sense on its own

EXAMPLE
<u>Fred looked pleased</u> when the sun started to appear.

Phrases

Phrase: a group of

words with either

no **v**........., no

subject or neither

          to the front

N......... **phrase**: contains

a noun and any words

that d.................... it

          the enormous red
          sunflower outside

Tenses & Linking Words

Conjunctions

.... conjunctions join two main clauses.

Use **FANBOYS** to remember them:

For And N..... B..... O..... Y..... S.....

> **EXAMPLE**
>
> I visited Iceland ....
>
> I didn't see any ice.

main clauses

Conjunctions can help your writing to **f**........ This is called cohesion.

> The café closed. The chef was ill. There was no coffee left.

> The café closed **because** the chef was ill **and** there was no coffee left.

Subordinating conjunctions

Subordinating conjunctions can go at the start of a sentence or in the middle.

Subordinating conjunctions introduce a **s**........................ claus

> **EXAMPLE**
>
> main clause
>
> Lois likes to read **while** she brushes her teeth.
>
> subordinate clause

Prepositions

Prepositions can tell you:

1 .... things are
Pip is **on** the rock.

2 When something happens
We stayed up .... sunse

3 .... something happen
We hid **because of** the rain

Linking Ideas & Paragraphs

Adverbial phrases tell you **h**......., when, where or how **o**........... something happens.

You can use adverbial phrases to make your sentences flow smoothly:

> Tomorrow evening, we're going to Inverness. We'll stop in Edinburgh on the way.

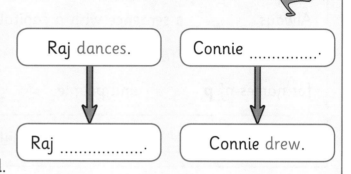

Present Tense & Past Tense

Use the simple **p**............... tense to write about something that happens regularly.

Use the simple **p**............... tense to write about something that's finished.

Raj dances.

Connie ....

Raj ....

Connie drew.

Verbs with 'ing'

To write about something that's still happening, use the .... form of 'to be' plus the main .... with 'ing' on the end.

are / am / is verb ing I am cooking an omelette.

'ing' verbs in the **p**........ are formed in the same way, but 'to be' has to be in the past tense.

They .... frowning.

The Present Perfect

The present perfect describes something that happened **r**...................

I have lost my key.

Use the **p**............... tense of 'to have' and a past tense form of the main **v**.........

He has seen a robin.

You can also use adverbs and adverbial phrases to link **p**........................ together smoothly.

EXAMPLE

Lola peered into the butterfly house through a tiny crack in the door.
→ Inside the butterfly house, butterflies of all shapes and sizes fluttered gracefully.

Punctuation Basics

Capital Letters

Always .... a sentence with a capital letter.

Use capital letters for the word 'I' and

for names of **p**............. and people.

Next ....riday, I am going to .....orway.

Commas in Lists

Use commas to

separate items

in a **l**........

Ending a Sentence

- Statements often .... in a full stop.

It's sunny today.

? .... always end in a question mark.

How are you?

! Exclamations, some **c**......................., and

sentences that are said **l**............ or with

strong emotion end in an exclamation mark.

That's fantastic!

Watch out!

Commas After...

Subordinate clauses

Only use a comma when the subordinate

clause comes .... the main clause.

Before I fall asleep, I count sheep.

.... **adverbials**

You need a comma when the adverbial

phrase is at the **s**........... of the sentence.

In the garden, there's a hungry dog.

Add a comma between each item in a list except the last two.

Separate the last two things with '.........' or '........'

EXAMPLE

I ate two apples, five cherries, seven raspberries and one banana today.

Use commas to make the meaning of a sentence **c**............

Otis asked his parents, Anna and Fiona.

This suggests Otis's parents are called Anna and Fiona.

Otis asked his parents............ and Fiona.

This suggests Otis asked his parents, as well as Anna and Fiona.

It's OK to put a comma before 'and' if the sentence is confusing without one.

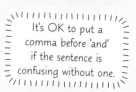

Paragraphs

Use a new paragraph for a:

1 new **s**............

2 new **t**........

3 new **p**..........

4 new **s**............

"Look!" squealed Olivia. "Can you see them?"

"They're so cute! I've never seen a fox in the daytime before," replied Tommasso.

The next day, they set up a camera in the garden to try to record the fox and her cubs.

At school, Olivia struggled to contain her excitement and couldn't wait to go home to check the footage. It was difficult to concentrate in lessons and she accidentally wrote the word 'fox' instead of 'box'.

Another thing distracting her was the thought of digging into her cheese sandwiches at lunchtime. She breathed a sigh of relief when the lunch bell rang.

More Punctuation

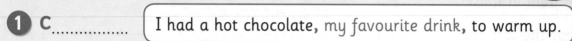

Adding Extra Information

Add extra information to a sentence using **p**.......... of:

1 C...............

I had a hot chocolate, my favourite drink, to warm up.

2 Brackets

Bess ...our first pet... was a black labrador.

> The extra information is sometimes called a parenthesis.

3 D..............

At the park — the one by the river — we had a picnic.

The punctuation goes on either side of the extra information.

The sentence should still make sense when the extra information is removed.

Apostrophes

M............. letters

The apostrophe shows where you've left letters out of a shortened word.

he is → he's   they are → ....

P............ possession

Use apostrophes to show possession for plural nouns.

If the plural noun ends in 's' you only add an apostrophe

the piglets..... mother

Use of apostrophes

S................... possession

To show that someone or something o..........

something, add an apostrophe and 's'.

the dog's nose   the bus..... wheels

> For singular nouns, you always add the 's', even if the word ends in 's' already.

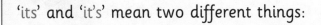

Its & It's

'its' and 'it's' mean two different things:

its = 'b................... to it'   The duck washed its feet.

it's = 'it is' or 'it ....'   .... a scary film.   It's been tiring.

nverted Commas & Punctuating Speech

If speech starts part-way through the sentence, add a .... before it.

Speech always **e**......... with a punctuation mark, which goes **i**............. the inverted commas.

Keith asked, "What's for tea?"

Inverted commas are also known as speech marks.

the plural noun
esn't end in 's',
ld an apostrophe
d 's'.

people..... beliefs

Speech usually starts with a .... letter, even when it isn't at the start of a sentence.

Punctuating Speech in Two Parts

Sometimes, speech is broken up by other information.

Don't forget to add punctuation at the end of your sentence.

"I want one thing," said Lyla, "and that's ice cream!"

The sentence hasn't finished yet, so you need a ....

You need a comma
b.............. the
second bit of speech.

You don't need a capital letter if the second bit of speech is part of the same sentence.

Grammar & Punctuation Quiz

Are you a grammar whizz and a punctuation pro? Find out with this quick quiz.

Key Words

1. Draw lines to match each word to what it does in a sentence.

pronoun	tells you if a noun is general or specific
determiner	introduces a subordinate clause
subordinating conjunction	replaces a noun

   3 marks

2. Fill in the gaps in the table below.

Term	Definition
adjective	....
....	a type of clause that has a subject and a verb, and makes sense on its own

   2 marks

Now Try These

3. Circle the box that is **not** a reason to start a new paragraph.

new speaker	new time	new sentence	new subject

   1 mark

4. Write down two co-ordinating conjunctions.

   .... and ....

   2 marks

5. Rewrite the sentence below, replacing the nouns with pronouns.

The princesses like to eat jam tarts.

....

2 marks

6. Circle the correct word to complete each sentence.

a) I **am / will** camping in the woods tonight.

b) Have we **ate / eaten** all the sausages?

c) I'm afraid he **have / has** already gone.

3 marks

7. Add in the missing comma to the sentence below.

When I was little I wanted to be a deep-sea diver.

1 mark

8. Fill in the gaps to complete the sentence below.

Prepositions can tell you .... things are, ...

something happens and .... something happens.

3 marks

9. Circle the correct option to complete each sentence.

a) I borrowed **Daisy's / Daisys** pen.

b) Have you seen the **girls' / girls's** tortoise?

2 marks

10. Rewrite the sentence below, adding in the missing punctuation.

I wish, she said "that I could fly.

....

4 marks

Score:

Prefixes, Suffixes & Word Endings

Key Words

Prefix: a letter or group of letters added to the **s**.......... of a **w**........

Suffix: a letter or group of letters added to the **e**...... of a **w**........

Root word: the word a **p**.......... or **s**............ is added to

'shul', 'shun' & 'shus'

1 The '**shul**' sound is often spelt:

'tial' after a **c**....................... 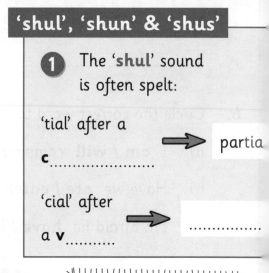 partia

'cial' after a **v**.......... ....

Hyphenating Prefixes

Use a hyphen to add a **p**..............:

1 to avoid confusion with similar words.

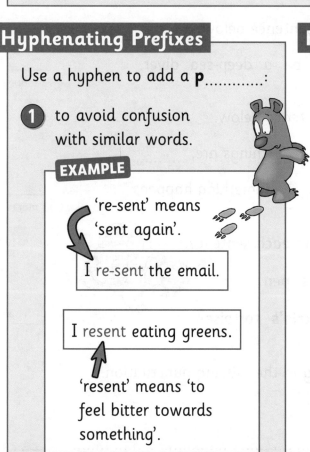

EXAMPLE

're-sent' means 'sent again'.

I re-sent the email.

I resent eating greens.

'resent' means 'to feel bitter towards something'.

2 if the **p**............ ends in a **v**.......... and the root word **b**............ with a vowel. co-exist

Prefixes

The spelling of the root word does not change when a prefix is added.

Prefix	Meaning	Example
under	too little	underfund
over	too much	....
....	not	nonsense
mid	middle	....
.........,' fore	before	preschool, ...
......, em	to put into	encircle, ...

'em' is used when the root word starts with 'b' or 'p'.

2 The '**shun**' sound is spelt:

There are some exceptions to these rules.

Root word ends...	Ending	Examples
't' or 'te'	'tion'	completion, ...
'c' or 'cs'	'..........'	clinician, politician
'd', 'de' or 'se'	'sion'	television, ...
'ss' or 'mit'	'ssion'	submission, ...

3 The '**shus**' sound can be spelt:

cious ⮕ vicious

tious ⮕ nutritious

If the root word **e**.........
in 'ce', the 'shus' sound is
usually spelt '.............'.

space ⮕ ....

More Word Endings

Sometimes, word endings sound similar, but are spelt differently.

The '**unce**' sound

balance   sci............

The '**unt**' sound

dist.........   talent

The '**uncy**' sound

vac.............   currency

'**able**', '**ible**',
'**ably**' and '**ibly**'

reliable   horr..........

reli............   horribly

Suffixes

Sometimes, the root word doesn't change when you add a suffix.

EXAMPLE

social + ise ⮕ ....

Nouns and adjectives often turn into verbs when suffixes are added to them.

But other times, the root does change.

EXAMPLE

terror + ify ⮕ ....

EXAMPLE

active + ate ⮕ ....

Confusing Words

'ei' & 'ie' Words

Use this rhyme to help you remember how to spell 'ei' and 'ie' words:

'i' before '...' except .... 'c' if the **v**.......... sound rhymes with bee.

shriek   Rhymes with bee and doesn't follow a 'c', so 'i' before 'e'.

rec.....ve   Rhymes with bee but follows a 'c', so '...' before '...'.

soc.....ty   Doesn't rhyme with bee but follows a 'c', so '...' before '...'.

> Some words don't follow the rule, e.g. seize. You just have to learn these words.

'ough' Words

Words containing the letters 'ough' can **s**............ very different. For example:

Here the 'ough' sounds like 'oh'. → dough, ...

Here the 'ough' sounds like 'or'. → thought, ...

Here the 'ough' sounds like 'uff'. → rough, ...

Here the 'ough' sounds like 'ow'. → drought, ...

Homophones

Homophones: words th
sound the **s**.........., but
have different meanings
and **s**...................

Silent Letters

Silent letters: letters that you don't **h**......... when you say a word

lamb	silent 'b'
....	silent 't'
gnome	silent 'g'
....	silent 'w'
....	silent 'k'
wheat	silent '....'
island	silent '....'
column	silent '....'

These are just examples — other letters can be silent too.

Unstressed Vowels

Unstressed vowels: vowel sounds that you can't **h**......... clearly

Sometimes they sound like a different vowel:

EXAMPLE

original $\xrightarrow{\text{sounds like}}$ originul

d...scribe $\xrightarrow{\text{sounds like}}$ discribe

Sometimes they sound like they're not there at all:

EXAMPLE

jewellery $\xrightarrow{\text{sounds like}}$ jewellry

fam...ly $\xrightarrow{\text{sounds like}}$ famly

past: the time gone by

passed: went by

past vs. passed

People did different jobs in the ....

I .... my friend's house earlier.

Spelling Quiz

Have a go at this quick smelling quiz. Sorry, spelling quiz.

1. Draw lines to match each word to its definition.

    suffix

    a vowel sound you can't hear clearly

    unstressed vowel

    the word a prefix or suffix is added to

    silent letter

    letters added to the end of a word

    root word

    a letter you don't hear when you say a word

    4 marks

2. What are homophones?

    ....

    ....

    1 mark

3. Underline the silent letter in each word below.

    a) knot   b) when   c) autumn

    3 marks

4. Add either 'ant' or 'ent' to the end of each
    word so that it is spelt correctly.

    a) sil.........   b) inf.........   c) const.........

    3 mark

16   Spelling

5. Underline the root word and circle the suffix in each word below.

   a)   p a y m e n t

   b)   f o l l o w e d

_____
4 marks

6. What do these prefixes mean?

   a)   'pre'   ....

   b)   'en'   ....

_____
2 marks

7. Circle the sound the 'ough' makes in 'tough'.

   'oh'   'or'   'uff'   'ow'

_____
1 mark

8. Fill in the gaps to complete the 'ei' and 'ie' spelling rule below.

   '.....' before '.....' except after '.....' if the

   vowel sound rhymes with bee.

_____
1 mark

9. Circle the correct words to complete the sentence below.

   There were three **offitials / officials** in charge of the

   martial / marcial arts competition.

_____
2 marks

10. Write down one reason to use a hyphen when adding a prefix.

   ....

   ....

_____
1 mark

Score: [   ]

Types of Text

Key Words

..................: texts about imaginary people and events

Non-fiction: texts that contain information and are based on **f**..........

..................: the reason a text has been written

Audience: **w**...... a text is for

Stories

See p.22-23 for more on features of stories.

Key features of stories:

- Usually have a **m**........ character and often a villain.
- Have a beginning, a **m**............ and an end.
- The purpose of stories is often to **e**.................. the reader.

There are many types of stories.

Types of Non-Fiction

Most non-fiction texts fit into one or more of these categories.

Recount
Retells events

Discussion text
Shares arguments **f**...... and against a topic

Persuasive text
P.................. people to think or do something

Types of non-fiction

Explanation text
Explains how a process works

Instruction text
Tells people **h**....... to do something

Report
Gives information on a topic, often in non-chronological **o**...........

Non-chronological means 'not in time order'.

EXAMPLE

1. An article debating whether phones should be allowed in scho

2. A fact file about Tudor Britain

Myths

explain ideas from the natural world

characters are often g......... or magical beings

A..................... stories

main character goes on a mission

often involve danger and excitement

S.................. fiction

often set in the future or a different world

plots use ideas from science and technology

.... text

R..................

Other Types of Fiction

Poems	often arranged into **v**.............
	use techniques like **r**..................... and **r**........................
P..........	designed to be performed
	include dialogue (characters talking)
	s........... directions to tell the actors what to do

Identifying Themes

Themes: the key ideas or messages in a text

Look for:

① **i**............ that appear multiple times.

② important topics.

EXAMPLE

Text: The Owl and the Pussy-Cat (nonsense poem)

Plot: An owl and a pussy-cat fall in love and get engaged on a boat. They buy a ring from a pig and get married.

.....................: love, marriage

Reading Skills

Working Out Meanings

If you're not sure what a word or phrase means:

1. Find clues in the text — other words you do understand.
2. See if it's part of a **w**......... **f**............. — use this to guess the meaning.
3. Look it up in a **d**...................

Language & Structure

Language

What effect do **w**............ and phrases have?

Wrinkling her brow, Ria spoke through gritted teet[h]

These words and phrases make Ria sound ....

Finding Information

Information can be stated directly:

Mount Everest is the highest point on Earth, reaching a height of 8849 metres.

The text tells you that Mount Everest is .... high.

Or you might have to use **c**.......... to work it out:

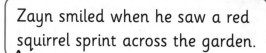

Zayn smiled when he saw a red squirrel sprint across the garden.

The text tells you that Zayn "smiled". This clue suggests he feels ....

Summarising Texts

Summarise the main **m**............... or ideas of a text.

Paragraph 1: Rome has lots to do.
Paragraph 2: It has delicious food.
Paragraph 3: The people are nice.

Summary: ....
....
....

Structure

1 How are the ideas grouped together?

2 Are there any points where things **c**............?

3 What order are **e**............ described in?

Comparing Texts

Make **c**........................ by looking for similarities and differences within or between texts.

Things you could compare:

1. the key **t**............
2. the use of language
3. characters — how they act and **f**........

Facts & Opinions

Facts: statements backed up by statistics or **e**..................

Polar bears can swim at speeds of up to 6 mph in water.

This information can be proven with evidence.

Opinions: personal **v**..........

I think oranges are delicious.

opinion word

Everyone loves oranges.

Opinions often use exaggerated language.

Making Predictions

When making predictions, think about:

What has **h**.................. so far?

How are the characters **f**............?

Are there clues about what's next?

Wei pitched the tent and then glanced up to the sky. A large, grey cloud loomed above him.

The "large, grey cloud" that "loomed above" suggests ....

Writing Fiction

Planning

Always **p**........ before you start writing. Think about:

1 | What? | plot

2 | **W**............? | setting

3 | **W**......? | characters

Plot

Basic story structure:

Beginning	the **s**.................. is set
Middle	a **p**.................. or conflict
E......	the **p**.................. is fixed

Starting a Story

Two great ways to begin:

1 in the middle of the **a**............

> Alvanah sprinted frantically away from the ghostly bat, trying not to anger it further.

2 with a character **s**..................

> "What was that noise?" Kareem asked timidly.

You can use speech to show a character's personality.

Setting

Use descriptive language to set the scene:

....

EXAMPLE

The stormy waves crashed onto the shore powerfully.

verb
adverb

S..................: when you say something is like something els

> Leo ran as fast as a cheetah.

Checking Your Writing

Always check for errors, and correct mistakes neatly.

was
It ~~were~~ raining cats and dogs

Characters

Show their p...........................

> **EXAMPLE**
>
> Ruby shuffled nervously into the room, anxiously playing with her long, curly hair.

and their **a**........................ .

Language Techniques

Onomatopoeia: when a word

s............. like what it describes

> Rex growled at the postman.

M....................: when you say

something is something else

> Abeke's story was a tangled web.

...mmon mistakes:

- **v**......... not matching the subject
- not staying in the same **t**...........
- forgetting to use paragraphs

Synonyms

Use a thesaurus to find interesting synonyms of common words.

> Synonyms are words with similar meanings.

> Synonyms of 'scary'
>
> ....
>
> ....
>
> ....

Story Writing Checklist

Make sure your story has:

 interesting characters & setting

 a problem to be fixed

 an effective start & **e**..............

 descriptive **l**...................

 correct **s**............... & grammar

Writing Non-Fiction

Formal Writing

1. uses formal l.................

   e.g. They were magnificent.

2. avoids contracted forms

   e.g. We will speak tomorrow.

3. avoids **e**........................ marks

   e.g. I started a new school.

Informal Writing

1. uses chatty language

   e.g. They were great.

2. can use contracted forms

   e.g. .... speak tomorrow.

3. can use exclamation marks

   e.g. I started a new school!

In informal writing you can add questions to the end of sentences, e.g. 'You like rock music, don't you?'

Informal Letters

Informal letters use a chatty and friendly style.

Use a new paragraph for each new point in a letter.

Their **f**.......... name

13 Dreary Lane
13th December

Your **a**.................

Hello Joe,
I wanted to tell you my news!

Lots of love,
Calum

Y......... first name   Friendly ending

Formal Letters

Formal letters follow strict rules.

Their **n**.......... and address

Your ....

Penny Black
8 Peacock Crescent

2 Robin Street
28th June

Dear Mrs Black,

I am writing to congratulate you on...

Yours sincerely,
Mr Bright ←   **s**.................

Your title an...

Begin with your reason for writing

Standard English

Always use Standard English in your writing.

Non-Standard English	Standard English
I seen my favourite film.	I .... my favourite film.
I ain't tried snorkelling.	I .... tried snorkelling.
Ben didn't want nothing.	Ben didn't want ....

Writing Information Texts

Layout devices make your writing clearer and more appealing.

slogan

H................

Bake with Badra

Bake it better

S..........................

Brush up on your baking skills

From whipping up a Victoria sponge to crafting perfect chocolate chip cookies, Badra will teach you to become a master baker in no time.

• 1 hour lesson — £20
• 2 hour lesson — £30

Underlining

B.............

P.............

If you don't know their name, begin your letter with 'Dear Sir/Madam' and end it with 'Yours faithfully'.

Reading & Writing Quiz

What's that? You want another quiz? Well, it's your lucky day...

Key Words

1. Fill in the gaps in the table below.

Term	Definition
....	the reason a text has been written
opinion	....
theme	....

3 marks

Now Try These

2. What kind of book should you use to find synonyms of words?

....

1 mark

3. Draw lines to match each example to its text type.

an article arguing for and
against making Fridays a day off   recount

                                                    discussion text

a recipe for a curry

                                                    instruction text

a biography of an actor

3 marks

4. Circle the word that is **not** an example of onomatopoeia.

oink   thud   laugh   splash

5. Rewrite these sentences using Standard English.

a) I dunno why he ain't happy today.

....

....

b) It's well strange — the robber didn't take nothing.

....

....

6. Fill in the gaps below using three terms from the box.

themes   mood   simile   characters

When comparing texts, you could compare the main

............................., the .... of each

text and how the .... behave.

7. Underline the two similes in the text below.

Niveen looked up at the sky, which was as clear and blue as the
unspoiled surface of a tropical lagoon. Laughing with delight,
she hurtled down the pavement on her scooter like a cannonball.

Score:

End of Year Quiz

Ready to test your knowledge with one last quiz? Time to show what you know.

1. Fill in the gaps in the table below.

Term	Definition
s...................... c......................	part of a sentence that gives extra information but doesn't make sense on its own
co-ordinating conjunction	....
P...................... P......................	a verb form that describes something that happened recently

3 mark

2. Draw lines to match each word to what it does. Use each option once.

abstract noun		describes a noun
modal verb		names ideas or feelings
adjective		shows how possible something is

3 mark

3. What is a fronted adverbial?

....

....

1 mar

4. Circle the correct spelling of each word below.

   a) The cows ran across the **field / feild** towards the farmer.

   b) Hanging from the **ceiling / cieling** was a huge spider.

   c) My favourite subjects are **Sceince / Science** and Art.

   _____
   3 marks

5. Add in the two missing commas in the sentence below.

   Our hotel which is next to the beach allows dogs.

   _____
   2 marks

6. Fill in the gaps in the table below.

Part of Story	What happens?
Beginning	The scene is set.
Middle	....
End	....

   _____
   2 marks

7. Write down a synonym of each word below.

   a) worried ....

   b) shy ....

   c) beautiful ....

   _____
   3 marks

8. Circle the correct homophone to complete each sentence below.

   a) My grandma will be annoyed if I **break / brake** her vase.

   b) There is a large **piece / peace** of lemon drizzle cake left.

   c) I'm not sure **witch / which** type of cheese is my favourite.

3 marks

9. Write down two layout devices you could use in an information text.

   ....

   ....

2 marks

10. True or false?
    Relative clauses always need a relative pronoun.

    ....

1 mark

11. Draw lines to match each type of story to one of its key features. Use each option once.

    science fiction   often involves a character on a mission

    adventure story   characters are often gods

    myth   often set in the future

3 mar

12. Write down one reason to use an apostrophe.

    ....

1 ma

13. Add each suffix to the root and write down the new word.

    a)   horror + ify   ....

    b)   captive + ate   ....

    c)   memory + ise   ....

_____
3 marks

14. Rewrite the sentences below, correcting the
punctuation mistakes. There are three to correct.

    "Can you see that" whispered Mo. "it's hiding behind the tree!

....

....

....

_____
3 marks

15. Read the extract from a text and answer the questions.

> The revolutionary Robo3000 loves meeting new people.
> Get yours today — it's the best robot money can buy!

    a)   What type of non-fiction text do you think this is from?

           ....

    b)   How do you know that the Robo3000 is friendly?

           ....

           ....

_____
2 marks

Score:

Answers

Grammar & Punctuation

Pages 2-3 — Grammar Basics

Nouns

Noun Type	Used to name...	Examples
Concrete	things you see, touch, smell or hear	mouse, cheese
Abstract	**ideas** or feelings	love, e.g. **positivity**
Collective	groups of people or things	a swarm of bees

Verbs

Verbs: **doing** or being words

Verbs change depending on **who** is doing the action.

He **walks**. They **walk**.

Modal verbs: show how certain or possible something is

Adjectives

Adjectives tell you more about a **noun**.

e.g. a **quiet** girl

Adverbs

1. **Verbs** — She calmly slept in bed.
2. Adjectives — e.g. He is **very** loud.
3. Adverbs — e.g. I spoke **really** quietly.

Pronouns

Pronouns replace **nouns**.

Henrik baked a cake, and he decorated **it**.

Relative pronouns introduce relative **clauses**.

Determiners

Determiners go in front of **nouns**.

e.g. I ate **an** orange.

Clauses

Main clause: has a subject and a verb, and makes sense on its own

Subordinate clause: gives extra **information** but doesn't make sense on its own

Relative Clauses

Relative clause: a subordinate clause often introduced by a relative **pronoun**

Relative clauses don't always have a relative **pronoun**.

Phrases

Phrase: a group of words with either no **verb**, no subject or neither

Noun phrase: contains a noun and any words that **describe** it

Pages 4-5 — Tenses & Linking Words

Conjunctions

Co-ordinating conjunctions join two main clauses.

For, And, **Nor**, **But**, **Or**, **Yet**, **So**

I visited Iceland **but / yet / and** I didn't see any ice.

Subordinating conjunctions introduce a **subordinate** clause.

Conjunctions can help your writing to **flow**.

Prepositions

1. **Where** things are
2. e.g. We stayed up **until** sunset.
3. **Why** something happens

Linking Ideas & Paragraphs

Adverbial phrases tell you **how**, when, where or how **often** something happens.

You can also use adverbs and adverbial phrases to link **paragraphs** together smoothly.

Present Tense & Past Tense

Use the simple **present** tense to write about something that happens regularly.

Use the simple **past** tense to write about something that's finished.

Raj dances. — Raj **danced**.

Connie **draws**. — Connie drew.

Verbs with 'ing'

To write about something that's still happening, use the **present** form of 'to be' plus the main **verb** with 'ing' on the end.

'ing' verbs in the **past** are formed in the same way, but 'to be' has to be in the past tense.

They **were** frowning.

The Present Perfect

The present perfect describes something that happened **recently**.

Use the **present** tense of 'to have' and a past tense form of the main **verb**.

Answers

Pages 6-7 — Punctuation Basics

Capital Letters

Always **start** (or **begin**) a sentence with a capital letter.

Use capital letters for the word 'I' and for names of **places** and people.

Next **F**riday, I am going to **N**orway.

Commas in Lists

Use commas to separate items in a **list**.

Separate the last two things with '**and**' or '**or**'.

Ending a Sentence

Statements often **end** in a full stop.

Questions always end in a question mark.

Exclamations, some **commands**, and sentences that are said **loudly** or with strong emotion end in an exclamation mark.

Commas After...

Only use a comma when the subordinate clause comes **before** the main clause.

Fronted adverbials

You need a comma when the adverbial phrase is at the **start** of the sentence.

Commas to Avoid Ambiguity

Use commas to make the meaning of a sentence **clear** (or **clearer**).

Otis asked his parents, **Anna,** and Fiona.

Paragraphs

1. new **speaker**
2. new **time**
3. new **place**
4. new **subject**

Pages 8-9 — More Punctuation

Adding Extra Information

Add extra information to a sentence using **pairs** of:

1. **Commas** — I had a hot chocolate, my favourite drink, to warm up.
2. **Brackets** — Bess **(**our first pet**)** was a black labrador.
3. **Dashes** — At the park — the one by the river — we had a picnic.

Apostrophes

Missing letters
they are → **they're**

Single (or **Singular**) possession
To show that someone or something **owns** something, add an apostrophe and 's'.

the bus**'s** wheels

Plural possession

the piglets**'** mother

the people**'s** beliefs

Its & It's

its = '**belonging** to it'
it's = 'it is' or 'it **has**'
It's a scary film.

Inverted Commas & Punctuating Speech

If speech starts part-way through the sentence, add a **comma** before it.

Speech always **ends** with a punctuation mark, which goes **inside** the inverted commas.

Speech usually starts with a **capital** letter, even when it isn't at the start of a sentence.

Punctuating Speech in Two Parts

The sentence hasn't finished yet, so you need a **comma**.

You need a comma **before** the second bit of speech.

Pages 10-11 — Grammar & Punctuation Quiz

Key Words

1. pronoun — replaces a noun
   determiner — tells you if a noun is general or specific
   subordinating conjunction — introduces a subordinate clause
   (1 mark for each)

2.

Term	Definition
adjective	e.g. **a word that describes a noun**
main clause	a type of clause that has a subject and a verb, and makes sense on its own

(1 mark for each)

Now Try These

3. new sentence (1 mark)
4. Any two from:
   for, and, nor, but, or, yet, so
   (1 mark for each, up to a maximum of 2 marks)

Answers

5. **They** like to eat **them**.
(1 mark for each)

6. a) I **am** camping in the woods tonight.
   b) Have we **eaten** all the sausages?
   c) I'm afraid he **has** already gone.
(1 mark for each)

7. When I was little**,** I wanted to be a deep-sea diver. (1 mark)

8. Prepositions can tell you **where** things are, **when** (or **why**) something happens and **why** (or **when**) something happens.
(1 mark for each)

9. a) I borrowed **Daisy's** pen.
   b) Have you seen the **girls'** tortoise?
(1 mark for each)

10. "I wish," she said, "that I could fly."
(1 mark for adding each punctuation mark correctly)

Spelling

Pages 12-13 — Prefixes, Suffixes & Word Endings

Key Words

Prefix: a letter or group of letters added to the **start** of a **word**

Suffix: a letter or group of letters added to the **end** of a **word**

Root word: the word a **prefix** or **suffix** is added to

Hyphenating Prefixes

Use a hyphen to add a **prefix**:

2. if the **prefix** ends in a **vowel** and the root word **begins** with a vowel.

Prefixes

Prefix	Meaning	Example
under	too little	underfund
over	too much	e.g. **overslept**
non	not	nonsense
mid	middle	e.g. **midway**
pre, fore	before	preschool, e.g. **forecast**
en, em	to put into	encircle, **embrace**

'shul', 'shun' & 'shus'

1. The 'shul' sound is often spelt: 'tial' after a **consonant** 'cial' after a **vowel** — e.g. **special**

2. The 'shun' sound is spelt:

Root word ends...	Ending	Examples
't' or 'te'	'tion'	completion, e.g. **action**
'c' or 'cs'	**'cian'**	clinician, politician
'd', 'de' or 'se'	'sion'	television, e.g. **decision**
'ss' or 'mit'	'ssion'	submission, e.g. **discussion**

3. If the root word **ends** in 'ce', the 'shus' sound is usually spelt **'cious'**.
space → **spacious**

More Word Endings

The 'unt' sound — dist**ant**

The 'unce' sound — sci**ence**

The 'uncy' sound — vac**ancy**

'able', 'ible', 'ably' and 'ibly' — horr**ible**, reli**ably**

Suffixes

social + ise → **socialise**

terror + ify → **terrify**

active + ate → **activate**

Pages 14-15 — Confusing Words

'ei' & 'ie' Words

'i' before 'e' except **after** 'c' if the **vowel** sound rhymes with bee.

rec**ei**ve — Rhymes with bee but follows a 'c', so 'e' before 'i'.

soc**ie**ty — Doesn't rhyme with bee but follows a 'c', so 'i' before 'e'.

'ough' Words

Words containing the letters 'ough' can **sound** very different.

dough, e.g. **although**

thought, e.g. **nought**

rough, e.g. **enough**

drought, e.g. **plough**

Homophones

Homophones: words that sound the **same**, but have different meanings and **spellings**

People did different jobs in the **past**

I **passed** my friend's house earlier.

Answers

Silent Letters

Silent letters: letters that you don't **hear** when you say a word

lamb	silent 'b'
e.g. **listen**	silent 't'
gnome	silent 'g'
e.g. **write**	silent 'w'
e.g. **knee**	silent 'k'
wheat	silent '**h**'
island	silent '**s**'
column	silent '**n**'

Unstressed Vowels

Unstressed vowels: vowel sounds that you can't **hear** clearly

describe — discribe

family — famly

Pages 16-17 — Spelling Quiz

Key Words

. suffix — letters added to the end of a word
unstressed vowel — a vowel sound you can't hear clearly
silent letter — a letter you don't hear when you say a word
root word — the word a prefix or suffix is added to
(1 mark for each)

. Any sensible definition, e.g. Words that sound the same but have different meanings and spellings. (1 mark)

Now Try These

3. a) k<u>n</u>ot
   b) w<u>h</u>en
   c) autum<u>n</u>
   (1 mark for each)

4. a) silent
   b) infant
   c) constant
   (1 mark for each)

5. a) root word: 'pay'
      suffix: 'ment'
      (1 mark for each)
   b) root word: 'follow'
      suffix: 'ed'
      (1 mark for each)

6. a) before
   b) to put into
   (1 mark for each)

7. 'uff' (1 mark)

8. 'i' before 'e' except after 'c' if the vowel sound rhymes with bee.
   (1 mark)

9. There were three **officials** in charge of the **martial** arts competition.
   (1 mark for each)

10. Any sensible answer, e.g. to avoid confusion with similar words
    OR:
    when the prefix ends in a vowel and the root word begins with a vowel
    (1 mark)

Reading & Writing

Pages 18-19 — Types of Text

Key Words

Fiction: texts about imaginary people and events

Non-fiction: texts that contain information and are based on **facts**

Purpose: the reason a text has been written

Audience: **who** a text is for

Stories

Key features of stories:

- Usually have a **main** character and often a villain.
- Have a beginning, a **middle** and an end.
- The purpose of stories is often to **entertain** the reader.

Myths

- characters are often **gods** or magical beings

Adventure (or **Action**) stories

Science fiction

Types of Non-Fiction

Persuasive text
Persuades people to think or do something

Discussion text
Shares arguments **for** and against a topic

Instruction text
Tells people **how** to do something

Report
Gives information on a topic, often in non-chronological **order**

Answers

An article debating whether phones should be allowed in school — **Discussion** text

A fact file about Tudor Britain — **Report**

Other Types of Fiction

Poems	often arranged into **verses**
	use techniques like **rhyme** and **repetition** (or **rhythm**)
Plays	**stage** directions to tell the actors what to do

Identifying Themes

1. **ideas** that appear multiple times.

Themes: love, marriage

Pages 20-21 — Reading Skills

Working Out Meanings

2. See if it's part of a **word family** — use this to guess the meaning.

3. Look it up in a **dictionary**.

Language & Structure

Language

What effect do **words** and phrases have?

These words and phrases make Ria sound e.g. **annoyed**.

Structure

2. Are there any points where things **change**?

3. What order are **events** described in?

Finding Information

The text tells you that Mount Everest is **8849 metres** high.

Or you might have to use **clues** to work it out:

The text tells you that Zayn "smiled". This clue suggests he feels e.g. **happy**.

Summarising Texts

Summarise the main **message** or ideas of a text.

Summary:
e.g. **Rome is a great place to visit.**

Facts & Opinions

Facts: statements backed up by statistics or **evidence**

Opinions: personal **views**

Comparing Texts

Make **comparisons** by looking for similarities and differences within or between texts.

Things you could compare:

1. the key **themes**

3. characters — how they act and **feel**

Making Predictions

What has **happened** so far?
How are the characters **feeling**?

The "large, grey cloud" that "loomed above" suggests
e.g. **it is about to rain.**

Pages 22-23 — Writing Fiction

Planning

Always **plan** before you start writing.

2. **Where?** setting

3. **Who?** characters

Plot

Basic story structure:

Beginning	the **scene** is set
Middle	a **problem** or conflict
End	the **problem** is fixed

Setting

stormy — **adjective**

Starting a Story

1. in the middle of the **action**

2. with a character **speaking**

Characters

Show their **personality** and their **appearance**.

Synonyms

e.g. **terrifying, frightening, horrifying**

Language Techniques

Onomatopoeia: when a word **sounds** like what it describes

Simile: when you say something is like something else

Metaphor: when you say something is something else

Checking Your Writing

1. **verb** not matching the subject

2. not staying in the same **tense**

Answers

Story Writing Checklist

- an effective start & **end(ing)**
- descriptive **language**
- correct **spelling** & grammar

Pages 24-25 — Writing Non-Fiction

Formal Writing

1. uses formal **language**
3. avoids **exclamation** marks

Informal Writing

2. can use contracted forms,
   e.g. **We'll** speak tomorrow.

Informal Letters

From left to right:
Their **first** name
Your first name
Your **address**

Formal Letters

From left to right:
Their **name** and address
Your **address**
Your title and **surname**

Standard English

saw my favourite film.
haven't (or **have not**)
tried snorkelling.
then didn't want **anything**.

Writing Information Texts

From top to bottom:
Heading
Subheading
Bullet Points

Pages 26-27 — Reading & Writing Quiz

Key Words

1.

Term	Definition
purpose	the reason a text has been written
opinion	e.g. **a personal view**
theme	e.g. **a key idea or message in a text**

(1 mark for each)

Now Try These

2. a thesaurus (1 mark)
3. an article arguing for and against making Fridays a day off — discussion text
   a recipe for a curry — instruction text
   a biography of an actor — recount
   (1 mark for each)
4. laugh (1 mark)
5. a) e.g. I **don't know** why he **isn't** happy today.
   (1 mark for each correction)
   b) e.g. It's **very** strange — the robber didn't take **anything**.
   (1 mark for each correction)
6. When comparing texts, you could compare the main **themes**, the **mood** of each text and how the **characters** behave.
   (1 mark for each)
7. You should have underlined:
   'as clear and blue as the unspoiled surface of a tropical lagoon'
   'like a cannonball'
   (1 mark for each)

Pages 28-31 — End of Year Quiz

Key Words

1.

Word	Definition
subordinate clause	part of a sentence that gives extra information but doesn't make sense on its own
co-ordinating conjunction	e.g. **a conjunction that joins two main clauses**
present perfect	a verb form that describes something that happened recently

(1 mark for each)

2. abstract noun — names ideas or feelings
   modal verb — shows how possible something is
   adjective — describes a noun
   (1 mark for each)
3. e.g. an adverbial phrase at the start of a sentence (1 mark)

Now Try These

4. a) The cows ran across the **field** towards the farmer.
   b) Hanging from the **ceiling** was a huge spider.
   c) My favourite subjects are **Science** and Art.
   (1 mark for each)
5. Our hotel**,** which is next to the beach**,** allows dogs.
   (1 mark for each)

Answers

6.

Part of Story	What happens?
Beginning	The scene is set.
Middle	e.g. **There's a problem or conflict.**
End	e.g. **The problem is fixed.**

(1 mark for each)

7. Any sensible answers, e.g.
   a) anxious
   b) timid
   c) pretty
   (1 mark for each)

8. a) My grandma will be annoyed if I **break** her vase.
   b) There is a large **piece** of lemon drizzle cake left.
   c) I'm not sure **which** type of cheese is my favourite.
   (1 mark for each)

9. Any sensible answers, e.g.
   heading
   subheadings
   bullet points
   tables
   pictures/diagrams
   underlining
   (1 mark for each, up to a maximum of 2 marks)

10. False
    (1 mark)

11. science fiction — often set in the future
    adventure story — often involves a character on a mission
    myth — characters are often gods
    (1 mark for each)

12. Any sensible answer, e.g.
    to show where letters are missing
    OR:
    to show who or what owns something
    (1 mark)

13. a) horrify
    b) captivate
    c) memorise
    (1 mark for each)

14. "Can you see that**?**" whispered Mo. "**I**t's hiding behind the tree!"
    (1 mark for correcting each mistake)

15. a) persuasive text / advert
    b) e.g. It "loves meeting new people".
    (1 mark for each)